Contents

Capital letters and full stops

Capital letters and full stops make your writing easier to read.

- Sentences always begin with a capital letter, for example A, B, C, D, E.

  One morning the three bears went for a walk. While they were out Goldilocks peeped inside their cottage.

- Most sentences end with a full stop.

  The spaceship roared towards the distant galaxy. Hutch peered through the porthole.

Always mark the beginning and end of every sentence you write.

Hutch's workout

1 Put the missing full stops in the following two sentences.

goldilocks   saw   three   bowls   of   porridge   she   felt   very   hungry

Write the first word of each sentence. Don't forget the capital letters!

2 Use the following words to make two sentences in the boxes below. Use capital letters and full stops.

one star was extra bright it had golden rings round it

Star points **Begin** every sentence with a **capital letter**.
End most sentences with a **full stop**.

Question marks

Question marks show that questions have been asked.

- Written questions always end with a question mark.

  Do you know who lives here?

  Where have they gone?

- Questions often begin with wh words: who, what, where, when, why.

  When will the spaceship arrive?

  What will it be like?

  Where will it land?

 Question marks help you to read expressively.

Hutch's workout

1 Read these sentences and add a question mark or full stop at the end of each one.

Why did Goldilocks go to the cottage

She sat on the biggest chair but it was too hard

Who likes porridge with salt

2 Here are two answers. Can you write the questions that go with them?

Nine planets travel round the Sun.

The Earth takes a year to travel round the Sun.

Exclamation marks

Exclamation marks follow shouts, cries, screams and yells.

- An exclamation is a strong feeling, for example Help! Surprise! Ouch!

> Ow! That's too hot.
>
> Bother! I've broken the chair.

- Use exclamation marks to show anger, surprise or joy.

> That's beautiful! (joy)
>
> Put that down at once! (anger)

 Use exclamation marks to show expression in your writing.

Hutch's workout

> What a lovely day!

1 Write out each exclamation in the boxes below.
(Don't forget capital letters and exclamation marks.)

oh dear	that's awful	look out	what a lovely day

2 Punctuate the end of the following sentences, using   ?   .   or   !

> Who ate the porridge

> My name is Baby Bear

> Goodness me

> How many stars are in the sky

Star points   Every sentence must end with a full stop, exclamation mark or question mark.

4

Commas in a list

A comma is a punctuation mark used inside a sentence.

- Commas are often used to separate items in a list. But don't put a comma before 'and'.

> Mother Bear bought sugar, salt, milk and bread in the supermarket.

- Commas are also used between people's names and numbers.

> Star, Hutch and Sky climbed into the rocket. "One, two, three, testing," a voice boomed over the radio.

Use commas between items in a list, numbers and names.

Hutch's workout

1 Mark the missing commas in the following two sentences.

> **Father Bear planted peas   beans   potatoes and carrots in his garden.**

> **Goldilocks counted one   two   three bowls.**

2 Put the missing commas in Star's checklist.

Checklist for spacemen

Pack clean socks   shirts   vests and jumpers.

Bring a toothbrush   flannel   hairbrush and towel.

Wear a coat   scarf   hat and gloves.

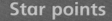
Star points   Commas are used inside sentences. Use them between items in a list.

Speech marks

Speech marks go round what characters say.

- They go at the beginning and end of words that are spoken.

  "I want my porridge."

- When you write speech you need to say who is talking.

  "I want my porridge," said Baby Bear.

  "Quick, the bone's here!" shouted Hutch.

- Don't use too much speech when you write. It can slow the story down and can become boring.

  "What do you want for tea tonight?" asked Mum.

  "I'll have beans on toast please," replied Pat.

Speech marks go round the words that people say.

Hutch's workout

1 Put the missing speech marks in the two sentences below.

There she is squeaked Baby Bear.

Starship to mission control said Hutch.

2 Turn these speech bubbles into sentences. (Don't forget the speech marks!)

Don't press that button!

It's all broken!

Star points   When characters talk, put speech marks round the words they actually say.

6

Punctuation practice

Punctuation makes your writing easier to read.

You have now learnt about capital letters, full stops, question marks, exclamation marks, commas in lists and speech marks. Complete the work below to check that you can remember them all.

Remember to mark the beginning and end of every sentence when you write.

Hutch's workout

Read through this story carefully. Listen out for sentences then put in the missing punctuation.

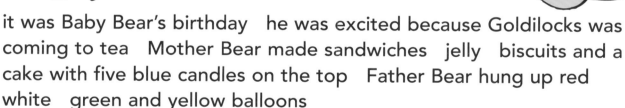

Baby Bear's birthday

it was Baby Bear's birthday   he was excited because Goldilocks was coming to tea   Mother Bear made sandwiches   jelly   biscuits and a cake with five blue candles on the top   Father Bear hung up red white   green and yellow balloons

when will Goldilocks get here   asked Baby Bear   I want my tea

she won't be long now   replied Mother Bear

here she comes   shouted Baby Bear and he rushed out to meet her   splat   he was in such a hurry that he fell over

don't cry   said Goldilocks   look I've got you a present

Star points Always check your writing for punctuation, especially the beginning and end of every sentence.

7

Vowels

There are five vowel letters: a e i o u.

- Recognising vowel sounds will help you to spell well.

- Vowels can make short sounds:

- Vowels can also make long sounds:

 Know the five vowels: a e i o u.

Hutch's workout

1 (Circle) all of the words with short vowel sounds.

shop	see	look
cat	go	first	brush
fly	brick	hen

2 Sort the following words by spelling patterns that make the long 'i' sound.

light   bite   high

cry   kite   try   quite

fly   night   sky

y	
i e	
igh	light

Star points   Learn to recognise short and long vowels in words – it will help you to spell well.

8

Blends

Blends can be difficult to hear.

- Blends often come at the beginning and end of words.

> Goldilocks crept up the stairs and went to sleep.

- Most blends have two letters and two sounds, but some have three.

> The engine screamed and spluttered as the rocket flew over the strange purple planet.

- Don't confuse blends with the digraphs ch, sh, th. (These also have two letters but only make one sound.)

> Make sure you hear and write all of the sounds in words containing blends.

Hutch's workout

1 Spell each of these words. (Listen hard because they all contain blends.)

_____ _____ _____ _____

2 Count the sounds in these words.
(Don't get tricked by counting the letters.)

chop	fish	milk	skip	blue
☐	☐	☐	☐	☐

step	blend	green	string	stamp
☐	☐	☐	☐	☐

Star points   Listen carefully to the sounds in words as you spell them.

Tricky words

Tricky words don't look as they sound.

- Some tricky words often trip us up, so we need to find ways to remember how to spell them.

> **Said** is a tricky word. It sounds like s-e-d. You can hear **s** and **d** so you need to find a way of remembering the **ai**.

- Try using a highlighter pen to mark the little words hiding inside words that you find difficult to spell.

> **Was** sounds like w-o-z. But can you see the little word **as** inside?
>
> **Could** sounds like c-u-d but the letters **ould** appear in lots of words so try to remember them as a pattern.

- Try making up a mnemonic – a word starting with each letter to make a catchy phrase.

> For **o-u-l-d** you could remember **oh y**ou **l**ucky **d**uck.

- Try mixing up magnetic letters on your fridge door then rearranging them, or writing a word in the air ten times with your finger.

> **Learn a range of spelling strategies to use with tricky words.**

Hutch's workout

1 Look for little words inside these words. Write them in the boxes below.

know	four	about	one	what

2 <u>Underline</u> the letter pattern that is the same in each of these words.

cough   dough   bought   plough   enough

Star points Tricky words need tricky strategies. Learn some words within words, spelling patterns and mnemonics.

Plurals

Plural means more than one.

- Most plurals are made by just adding 's'.

> Mother Bear washed up three bowls, three plates and three spoons.

- Words that end with shushing, hissing or buzzing sounds need 'es'.

> The three friends checked their wat**ch**es as they landed. They saw that the planet was covered with strange purple bu**sh**es.

- Another check for es endings is to clap – bush, bushes. An extra clap means add 'es'.

> For most plural words add 's'. Check for 'es' by clapping.

Hutch's workout

1 Add 's' or 'es' to make plurals.

Goldilocks saw flower___, tree___ and animal___ on her walk through the forest.

Sky put sandwich___, glass___ and dish___ in their picnic box___.

2 Write the plural words under each of the following pictures.

_____ _____ _____ _____

Star points   Listen for missing plurals when you read your work through.

11

'ed' endings

'ed' endings show that something has already happened (past tense).

- To change many verbs from present to past tense, just add 'ed'.

> **Happening now (present tense):** The bears <u>walk</u> through the forest.
>
> **Already happened (past tense):** The bears <u>walk</u>ed through the forest.

- Sometimes we need to add an extra letter before 'ed', for example when a single letter follows a short vowel.

> trip - trip**p**ed   spot - spot**t**ed
>
> pat - pat**t**ed   slip - slip**p**ed

- If there are already two letters after the vowel, don't add more.

> hi**ss** - hissed   cra**sh** - crashed
>
> fi**ll** - filled   cra**ck** - cracked

 Hear a short vowel and double the final letter before you add 'ed'.

Hutch's workout

1 Sort the following verbs into the two boxes below.

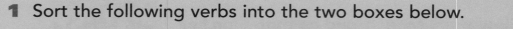
jump bump scrub melt watch brush wish trip stop wait trim peg

Just add 'ed'	Double final letter then add 'ed'

2 Write the following sentence in the past tense by adding 'ed' to the <u>underlined</u> verb.

The children <u>wait</u> for the spaceship.

Star points   Add 'ed' to verbs to make the past tense.
Double the last letter after a short vowel.

'ing' endings

'ing' at the end of a verb often shows it is happening now.

- Things happening now are in the present tense.

  > I am reading this workbook (I'm doing it now - present tense).

- To change many verbs just add 'ing', for example after 'y' or if two consonants follow a vowel.

  > play - playing   jump - jumping
  > find - finding   add - adding

- When a word ends with 'e', chop off the 'e' before you add 'ing'.

  > hope - hoping   like - liking
  > save - saving   raise - raising

- Sometimes we add an extra letter before 'ing', for example with short vowel sounds.

  > spot - spotting   hit - hitting
  > rub - rubbing   bat - batting

 When adding 'ing', listen for short vowels and look out for 'e'.

Hutch's workout

1 Spot what is wrong with these 'ing' words. Write them correctly in the boxes.

Baby Bear is hoping and skiping with his new rope.

Sky is rideing his moon buggy. He is takeing some rocks to the spaceship.

2 Add 'ing' to these words but remember what happens when you see an 'e'.

try _____   sleep _____   hit _____   bake _____

Star points   When adding 'ing' remember to take off the final 'e'.

13

Spelling practice

Check spelling with your eyes and ask yourself - does it look right?

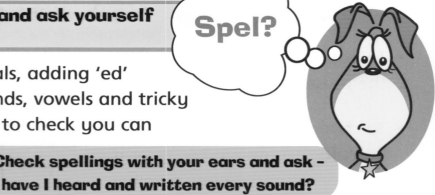

Spel?

You've learnt about making plurals, adding 'ed' or 'ing' to the ends of words, blends, vowels and tricky words. Complete the work below to check you can remember them all.

Check spellings with your ears and ask - have I heard and written every sound?

Hutch's workout

1 Spell the words that go with each picture.

 _____

 _____

 _____

 _____

 _____

 _____

 _____

 _____

 _____

2 Write each word with the two different endings.

Spell

Word	Add 'ing'	Add 'ed'
ask	asking	asked
look		
stop		
tape		
crush		
skip		
whine		
rub		

Star points Always check your spellings using your eyes and ears.

14

Playing with words

Choose words carefully to make your writing interesting.

- Words that begin with the same sound create a special effect, called alliteration.

> The **b**ears **b**ounced the **b**ig **b**all.
>
> **St**ars **gl**istened and **gl**eamed in the black sky.
>
> Be careful not to use it too often though!

- Words that make noises also create effect.

> **Splash!** The rocket landed in an enormous puddle.
>
> **Shush!** There's a little girl asleep in bed.

 Listen to your writing to hear the effect you make with words.

Hutch's workout

1 Choose words to create alliteration.

It was dark and _____ in the middle of the forest.

Star's fur was soft and _____ after her bath.

The _____ rocket landed safely.

> warm
> cold
> silky
> damp
> green
> red

2 Choose noisy words to finish these sentences.

The fire _____ in the grate.

'Please come and play with me,' _____ the dog.

The waves _____ over the rocks.

> crashed   woofed
> splashed   crackled
> burned   said

Star points When writing, choose words carefully. Listen to their effect when you read your work aloud.

Words instead of 'said'

Too many 'saids' make your writing sound dull.

- These sentences sound boring.

> 'Someone's been eating my porridge,' said Father Bear.
>
> 'Someone's been eating my porridge,' said Mother Bear.
>
> 'Someone's been eating my porridge,' said Baby Bear.

- Use speech verbs that describe how characters feel to make the text more interesting.

> 'Someone's been eating my porridge,' growled Father Bear.
>
> 'Someone's been eating my porridge,' moaned Mother Bear.
>
> 'Someone's been eating my porridge,' sobbed Baby Bear.

> Watch out for too many 'saids' - use words that show how characters are feeling.

Hutch's workout

whispered
roared
screamed
shouted
cried
whimpered

1 Find a better word than 'said' for each sentence. Choose one from the box or use one of your own.

The huge space monster moved towards the rocket.

'I'm coming to get you,' it said.

'I'm scared,' said Hutch.

'So am I,' said Star.

'I'm off,' said Fly.

2 Make a list of alternatives for 'said' – find some when you read.

> **Star points** Don't use 'said' too many times – it's dull. Use speech verbs that describe how the characters feel.

Pronouns

Names of people, places and things (nouns) sound wrong if overused.

- These sentences sound stodgy and boring because the names of the characters are repeated.

> Goldilocks **went upstairs.**
> Goldilocks **saw three beds.**
> Star **and** Hutch **climbed out of the rocket.**
> Star **and** Hutch **gazed around in amazement.**

- Pronouns are little words like she, he and **they** that can be used instead of names.

> **Goldilocks went upstairs.**
> She **saw three beds.**
> **Star and Hutch climbed out of the rocket.**
> They **gazed around in amazement.**

- It can be used to replace the names of places and objects.

> London **is a huge city.** It **is always busy.**
> **They gazed around in amazement.**

 Use pronouns to replace repeated nouns.

Hutch's workout

Use pronouns to improve these sentences. <u>Underline</u> the word or words that you want to change, then write the correct pronoun in each box.

| <u>it</u> | <u>she</u> | <u>he</u> | <u>them</u> | <u>they</u> |

1 **The three bears came home. The three bears felt tired.**

2 **The rocket was ready to fly. The rocket took off.**

3 **Star felt the engines throb. Star was pleased to be going.**

Star points Repeated nouns sound stodgy. Replace them with pronouns.

Connectives

Connectives are words that join ideas together.

- One of the most useful connectives is 'and'.

> Hutch and Sky
>
> fish and chips

- But don't use 'and' too often – it becomes boring.

> The bears went inside and saw the broken chair and Baby Bear cried and Father Bear was cross.

- Other connectives include: but, so, or, since, while, if, because. Some connectives can even be used to begin a sentence.

> 'Don't press that button because the engine will stop,' screamed Fly. If you really want to be helpful, pull the handle.

 Use connectives to join your ideas.

Hutch's workout

1 Choose the best connectives from the box to join these ideas together.

> but   if   or   because   suddenly
> so   that   also   and   after

Goldilocks liked sugar _____ she loved honey best.

Sky flew up high _____ she wanted to see where Hutch was hiding.

2 Use your own ideas to finish these two sentences.

I always clean my teeth after _____

I do some writing every day so that _____

Star points Use connectives to join your ideas, but don't use 'and' too often.

Time connectives

Use time connectives to order your work.

- Time connectives link sentences in time order.

> First **Goldilocks ate some porridge** then **she sat down.** Next **she went upstairs and** after that **she went to bed.**

- They are often used in instructions.

> First **get a large mixing bowl.**
> Next **pour in the ingredients.**
> After that **mix everything together.**

Use time connectives to link sentences together.

Hutch's workout

1 Fill in the following gaps with a time connective from the box.

How to fly a spaceship

	check the fuel.
	strap yourself in.
	turn on the engine.

finally
first
next

2 Sort out these muddled sentences, then write them in the correct order.

Our class outing
Then we looked round the farm. **First of all** we had a long coach ride.
Last of all we went to the shop. **After that** we had our lunch.

Star points   Use time connectives to order ideas.

Sentences

Improve your writing by using words that give extra information.

- Some sentences sound quite ordinary or dull.

> The three bears walked through the woods.

- 'Walked' doesn't really tell us very much. Try using a different word.

> The three bears strolled through the woods.
>
> The three bears hurried through the woods.

- You could also change 'woods' for a more precise word.

> The three bears sneaked through the forest.

Improve your writing by changing words rather than adding extra ones.

Hutch's workout

1 Change the <u>underlined</u> words for other words, to give extra information.

Goldilocks <u>looked</u> at the three bears.

The rocket <u>flew</u> to the new planet.

Hutch <u>lay</u> in her kennel.

zoomed	whizzed
peeped	relaxed
settled	rested
gazed	lounged
soared	glanced

2 Change the <u>underlined</u> words to more precise words.

The <u>building</u> was just down the lane.

The <u>garden</u> was full of <u>plants</u>.

The <u>man</u> knocked at the door.

weeds	wizard
factory	flowers
cottage	soldier
policeman	shop
castle	bushes

Star points Choose words carefully when you write.
Use words that give extra information.

Checking for sense

Always read your writing through when you finish.

- It's easy to miss words out, especially little ones.

> Goldilocks tasted ____ first bowl of porridge. 'Uh,' she gasped, 'It's much ____ hot.'
>
> Oh dear, I missed out 'the' and 'too'.

- Sometimes we use the wrong word.

> Hutch were very excited and called Sky and Star. They was really pleased to hear from him. 'were' and 'was' sound wrong - they need swapping over.

 Keep rereading your work to check if it sounds right.

Hutch's workout

1 Mark the missing words with a ⬆ then write them in the empty boxes.

Goldilocks tried the second bowl but was too sweet.

She tried third bowl and it was just right.

2 <u>Underline</u> the words that sound wrong, then write them correctly in the boxes.

'I are going to take a photo,' said Hutch.

'Don't forget I is watching,' laughed Sky.

Star points Keep rereading your writing. Ask yourself – Does it sound right? Does it make sense?

Write an exciting sentence that makes your reader want to read on.

- Begin with time.

> Once upon a time there was a little girl called Goldilocks.
>
> On Thursday George lost his hamster.

- Begin with a name.

> Hutch jumped out of bed.
>
> The King had a problem.

- Begin with a question.

> 'Where's my spacesuit?' yelled Sky.
>
> 'What's your new teacher like?' asked Nan.

 Make your first sentence a good one.

Hutch's workout

1 Draw lines to join the start to the end of these opening sentences.

'Why did you do that?'   play football.

On the first day of term   yelled Kim.

Danny didn't want to   Jack woke up early.

2 Finish each of these opening sentences.

Early one morning _____

Jo felt sad because _____

Star points The first sentence of a story is really important.
It must make the reader want to read on.

Story settings

The setting is where a story or event takes place.

- Settings are important. They help the reader to see, hear and feel what is happening.

- Some sentences say where a story is set, but add little else.

> In the forest **stood a cottage.**

- Carefully chosen words develop a setting. Words like 'dark', 'cold' or 'old' make a place sound creepy.

> **Deep in the forest stood a shabby,** old **cottage.**

- Bright colours, sunshine or flowers make settings feel safe.

> **At the edge of the forest stood a pretty, white cottage.**

Choose words carefully to create an effective setting.

Hutch's workout

1 Sort the following into safe words and scary words.

freezing	happy	trembling	beautiful	white	smell
strange	sparkling	light	shaking	grey	frightening
damp	warm	old	dark	soft	peaceful

safe

scary

2 Add extra words to make this setting sound scary.

The cave was _____ and _____.

Hutch could hear a _____ noise nearby.

He wanted to go back to the rocket.

Star points   Spend time planning your setting.
Make it add something to your story.

23

Characters

Characters are the people (or animals) in a story.

- You can describe what characters look like.

> Goldilocks had big blue eyes and long golden hair.
>
> His fur was silky and his ears were floppy.

- You can describe what characters are doing.

> She hung her head and began to cry.
>
> His hands were shaking as he opened the box.

- You can describe how characters are feeling.

> Hutch was so happy he thought he might burst.
>
> Goldilocks was so scared she jumped out of the window.

 **Make your characters come alive - use description.**

Hutch's workout

1 Write a sentence to describe what Hutch looks like.

2 Write a sentence to describe what he is doing.

3 Write a sentence to describe how he is feeling.

4 Choose another character and write three sentences about him/her.

Star points Bring your characters to life – you can say what they look like, what they are doing and how they are feeling.

Story endings

Endings should round off your writing.

- Always try to link the story ending with the beginning.

> **Beginning: Once upon a time there was a little girl called Goldilocks who went for a walk in the forest.**

> **Ending: So Goldilocks ran through the forest and the three bears never ever saw her again.**

- It's good to use words from the title in your ending, if you can.

The amazing rocket

Blast off! The rocket raced away - Hutch, Sky and Star were off on another adventure ...

... 'That rocket really was amazing,' laughed Hutch.

 Link the end of your story with the beginning.

Hutch's workout

1 Draw a line to match each beginning with an ending.

> **The clock struck midnight. 'Boo hoo,' cried the monster.**

> **'That's the best present ever!' 'Woof!' barked Rover.**

> **Mary wanted a puppy more than anything else in the world.**

> **So the monster had a friend and he never ever cried again.**

2 Write an ending to go with this beginning.

> **The elephant who wanted to shrink**
> 'It's not fair,' trumpeted Nelly, 'I'm always too big to join in the games. I wish I could shrink.'
>
> 'Well, I might be able to help you,' squeaked a little voice, 'Try drinking this!'

Star points Plan your ending before you start writing.
Make it link to the beginning.

Make a note of your ideas to help you remember them.

An adventure with Star, Sky and Hutch

Look back through the book for some extra information about these characters.

The three friends are about to set off on yet another adventure. You need to decide:

- where they are going
- what they will find when they get there
- how they get home again.

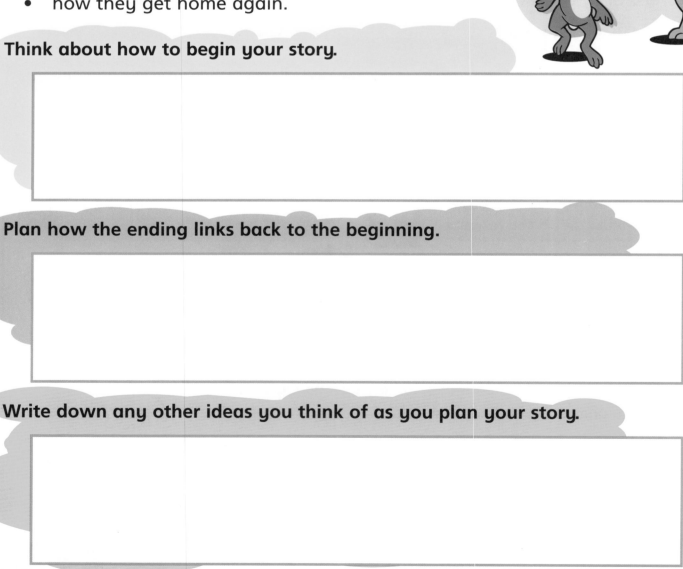

Think about how to begin your story.

Plan how the ending links back to the beginning.

Write down any other ideas you think of as you plan your story.

Always lay out your letter carefully.

Here is a letter from the three bears to Goldilocks.
Look carefully at the way it is laid out.

The White Cottage

Pebble Path

Deep Forest

23rd June 2002

Dear little girl,

We are sorry if we frightened you yesterday but we were really surprised to find you asleep in Baby Bear's bed. Did your mummy know that you had gone into a strange house? I'm sure she has told you not to do that.

Baby Bear was sad that you had eaten his breakfast and broken his chair but he had some cornflakes instead and Father Bear stuck his chair back together, so it's **OK** now.

Baby Bear has got a new book about spacemen and he wants to show you the pictures. Please come again but this time ask your mummy first.

Lots of love

from

The three bears

Star points   Letters need an address, date, greeting
and signing off – don't forget them.

Laying out a letter 2

There are four things to remember when laying out a letter.

1 Write the address in the top right hand corner. This will be your own address if the letter is from you, or could be a made up address if the letter is from a story character.

201 High Street
Barnhill
SL2 5DZ

2 Write the date under the address.

22nd May 2002

3 Write your greeting – begin with Dear, for example:
Dear Mr Wolf, Dear Nanny.

4 Write your letter. Think about who you are writing to (your audience) and try to order your writing so it is easy to follow.

 Remember who you are writing your letter to - use I, we and you.

Hutch's workout

1 Pretend you are writing to Goldilocks.

Write your address and today's date here. ➡

Write your greeting here.

Humm.....

2 Continue with this opening – decide what you are telling Goldilocks.

I am writing to tell you that . . .

Star points The layout of a letter is very important.
Remember the four things you must include.

28

> **Make a note of your ideas to help you remember them.**

A letter to the three bears

The three bears have invited you to tea. Think about three things that you will say to them in your reply. Don't forget to thank them for inviting you.

1

2

3

Write down some interesting words to use in your letter.

You will need to think about:

- how to start your letter
- how to arrange your writing
- how to join your ideas together
- how to end your letter.

Idea 1

the ending

the start

Idea 2

Instructions tell you how to do something.

Here is the recipe that Mother Bear uses to make porridge.

How to make porridge

Ingredients

- 1 cup of porridge oats
- 3 cups of water or milk
- pinch of salt

1 Put the porridge oats into a heavy-based saucepan.

2 Pour on the water or milk.

3 Add the salt.

4 Stir thoroughly.

5 Cook over a gentle heat for 10–15 minutes.

6 Mix vigorously as the mixture thickens, to prevent it sticking.

7 Stand for 3 minutes before serving.

Serve with salt, sugar, cream or syrup.

Serves 2–3

Star points   Instructions tell you how to do something. They are laid out in a certain way, written in the present tense using short, direct sentences.

There are three things to remember when writing instructions.

1 Always start with a heading that states your goal. This could begin with How to . . . .

> How to **make a cup of tea.**
>
> How to **mend a puncture.**

2 Write a list of ingredients or materials.

> **Ingredients:**
>
> 1 tea bag in a cup
> boiling water
> milk and sugar to taste

> **Materials:**
>
> puncture repair kit
> bowl of water
> tyre levers

3 Write the instructions in order. Use numbers, bullet points, letters or words. Use short sentences with no flowery adjectives.

> **Remember instructions need: 1** heading,
> **2** list of materials, **3** ordered steps.

Hutch's workout

1 Which of these could be headings for instructions? (✔ or ✗)

How to look after your pet hamster ☐

My Town - the past 50 years ☐

How to clean your teeth ☐

2 Do the instructions or materials come after the heading? ☐

3 Put these instructions in the correct order.

Read a story.	a)
Go to sleep.	b)
Get into bed.	c)
Put on your night clothes.	d)
Turn off the light.	e)

Star points Instructions have a heading, list of materials and clearly ordered steps.

Make a note of your ideas to help you remember them.

How to grow mustard and cress

You are going to write a set of instructions showing how to grow mustard and cress. You may need to grow some mustard and cress yourself before you write the instructions!

You need to think about:

- how to set out the instructions
- how to make them easy to follow
- how to use diagrams and labels.

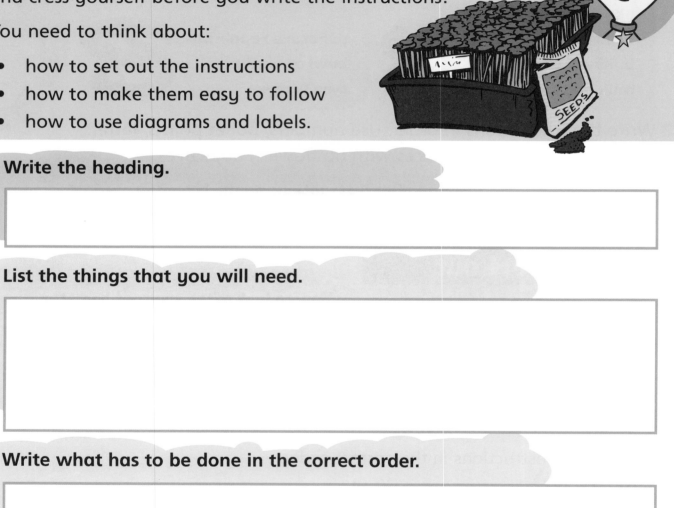

Write the heading.

List the things that you will need.

Write what has to be done in the correct order.

Star points   Remember your reader. Keep your writing clear and easy to follow.

Indexes and glossaries

Indexes and glossaries are arranged in alphabetical order.

- You find indexes and glossaries in information books.

- An index helps you find information. Topics are arranged in alphabetical order and the page numbers are written next to them. So to find out about fish you would turn to page 13.

- A glossary explains words that you might not know. The words are arranged in alphabetical order.

Index	
Birds	24
Fish	13
Mammals	17
Wild animals	11
Zoos	26

Glossary

Mammals	- animals with warm blood like us, that feed their young with milk.
Reptiles	- cold blooded animals like snakes with scaly skin, that lay eggs.

 Indexes and glossaries help you to use information books.

Hutch's workout

1 Sort the following words from a book about space alphabetically and then write them in the index.

Earth
Sun Moon
Pluto
Rocket

Index	
_____	26
_____	17
_____	11
_____	15
_____	29

2 Draw a line to match these words from a glossary with their definitions.

Earth	The smallest planet in our Solar System - furthest from the Sun.
Pluto	The planet with rings round it - sixth furthest from the Sun.
Saturn	The planet where we live - third furthest from the Sun.

Star points You use the index and glossary in non-fiction books to help you find and understand the information.

Information texts explain the way things are.

Baby Bear wanted to grow some plants.
Here are some pages from a book about plants.

Title **Growing Plants in Pots**
M R Greenfingers

Author or Publisher

Contents

Gardening in pots   3

Creative pots   6

Planting your pots   8

Looking after
your pots   10

1

Glossary

Compost: special soil for growing plants

Foliage: leaves and stems

Shrub: woody plant

Terracotta: brownish-red pottery

11

Index

Annuals   5

Bulbs   6

Compost   9

Edible plants   6

Terracotta pots   9

12

Gardening in pots

Why pots?

Everyone can grow plants in pots. They are fun to watch, don't take up much space and are easy to look after.

Which plants?

Almost anything can be grown in pots. Small trees, shrubs and bushes, flowers, even vegetables and salads will grow well with the right care.

3

Planting your own pots

Planting properly

Buy a pot that is big enough for the plants once they are fully-grown. Make sure there are drainage holes in the bottom of the pot and use a good quality compost.

1 Fill the pot loosely with compost.

2 Lower the plant into the pot and firm in.

3 Water well.

Remember that pot plants need regular watering and feeding.

8

Star points   Information books are carefully laid out to help readers find things out easily.

Writing an information booklet

There are five steps to remember when writing an information booklet.

Before starting you need to prepare the paper to make your booklet, and decide on the size and number of pages.

1 Carefully choose a title which sums up what the booklet is about – try to keep it short. Write it clearly and boldly on the front cover.

LOOKING AFTER GOLDFISH

2 Write a heading for each page.

Preparing the tank

Choosing a goldfish

3 Number the pages and list your contents.

4 Write information on each page matched to the headings. Keep your writing clear and direct. You can include sub-headings, diagrams, labels and captions.

5 Write your glossary and index (see the examples on page 34).

 Check that your booklet is clearly laid out and easy to follow.

Hutch's workout

1 Draw a line to match the following page headings with their opening sentences.

Choosing your hamster

What are stars made of?

Why we need teeth

A lot of the food we eat is too big to swallow.

Go to a well-known pet shop and talk to an assistant.

Stars are made from burning gases.

2 Collect page headings from a range of information books and sort them into different styles, e.g. questions, not questions. Use the ideas in your own writing.

Star points When you write information booklets, check that you use the same style of writing all the way through.

Make a note of your ideas to help you remember them.

An information booklet about bears

You are going to write an information booklet about bears. You may need to read some books about bears before you begin.

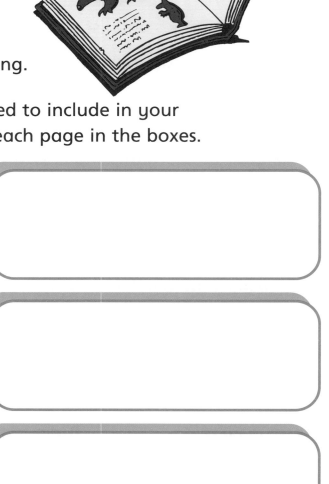

You need to think about:

- how to set out your information
- how to make the information clear
- how to make your booklet interesting.

Think about the information you will need to include in your booklet and then write the heading for each page in the boxes.

Star points Remember all the ways you can help readers find things more easily in your booklet.

Read everything very carefully at least twice before answering the questions.

There are four ways to answer comprehension questions.

One way is to tick the box that contains the right answer.

Read the following piece of writing two or three times.

One morning Mother Bear went to the shop to buy some beans.

On the way she met Mrs Tiger.

'Lovely day today,' she said, and hurried on her way.

Where did Mother Bear go? ← **This is the question**

☐ to meet Mrs Tiger ☐ to the shop

☐ to the forest ☐ for a walk

Did you decide that Mother Bear was going to the shop? Well done! Now tick the box.

Check the answer carefully before you tick the box.

Hutch's workout

Read this piece of writing and then answer the question by ticking one box.

Porridge is made from oats. Oats are cereals. Farmers grow lots of different cereals on their farms. One of the best-known cereals is wheat. It is used to make bread.

What is porridge made from?

☐ cereal   ☐ bread   ☐ wheat   ☐ oats

Star points When you answer questions like these tick one box only. If you make a mistake, don't worry; cross it out and tick another box.

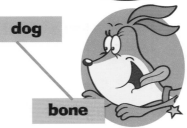

Always make sure you understand the question. Read it two or three times.

Another way to answer comprehension questions is to match parts of an answer by drawing a line between them.

Read the following piece of writing carefully.

> Baby Bear was helping in the garden. He pulled up weeds and put them in the barrow, he picked some beans and put them in a saucepan then he swept up the leaves and put them on the bonfire.

Where did Baby Bear put each of these things? Draw lines to match the boxes.

weeds	in a saucepan
beans	on the bonfire
leaves	in the barrow

Did you match beans with in the saucepan and leaves with on the bonfire? Well done!

Keep rereading the text to check your answers.

Hutch's workout

Read this piece of writing then answer the questions by joining the boxes.

> Wild animals make their homes in many different places. Rabbits live in holes under the ground, birds make nests in trees and bushes, and wild bears often live in caves.

Where do these animals live? Draw lines to match the boxes.

rabbits	in trees and bushes
birds	in caves
wild bears	under the ground

Star points   It's a good idea to use a ruler to draw the lines.

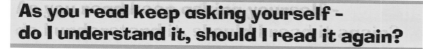

**As you read keep asking yourself –
do I understand it, should I read it again?**

Some questions ask you to **tick** or **cross** boxes
to show your answers.

Read the following piece of writing carefully.

To make an information booklet you need:

- 2 pieces of A4 paper
- a stapler and staples
- a pencil and ruler
- crayons or felt-tip pens.

Do you need each of these things?

Put a ✔ or ✗ in each box.

some staples	
a pair of scissors	
some glue	
a pencil	

Did you read the list very carefully and ✔ some staples
and a pencil? The list does not say scissors or glue
so you should have put a ✗ by them.

**Read carefully. Keep
checking the text
against the table.**

Hutch's workout

Read this piece of writing then answer the questions
by putting a ✔ or ✗ in each box.

Keeping healthy

To keep your body healthy you should eat plenty of fruit
and vegetables. Try not to eat too many sweets and crisps and don't drink
too many fizzy drinks. When you are thirsty drink milk, water or fruit juice.

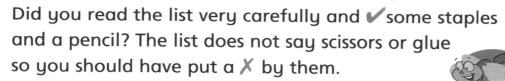

Which food and drink helps to keep you healthy? Put a ✔ or ✗ in each box.

sweets			fruit	
milk			fizzy drink	

Star points Make sure you put a tick or a cross
in each box.

39

As you read keep asking yourself - do I understand it, should I read it again?

Sometimes you are asked to answer by writing on a line.

Read the following piece of writing carefully.

1 _____

> Goldilocks was terrified. She ran and ran through the forest, glancing over her shoulder every few minutes, to see if the bears were following.
>
> At last she got home. 'Oh Mum,' she cried, 'You'll never guess where I've been!'

Which word tells you that Goldilocks was frightened?
(Write your answer on the line.)

_____

Did you find the word 'terrified'? That means the same as frightened so you should have written 'terrified' on the line.

 Always read everything carefully.

Hutch's workout

Read the writing in the box and then answer the question by writing on the line below.

Making jelly

Break the jelly square into pieces, put the pieces in a glass bowl and pour on a pint of boiling water. (Ask a grown up to help you with this.) Stir thoroughly until all the jelly pieces have dissolved. Leave the mixture to cool.

How much boiling water do you need to make the jelly?

_____

Star points Write your answers clearly so that someone else can read them.

'Hurry up and tidy your toys please,' called mum. 'It's nearly tea time.'

'Bother,' grumbled Steven, who was in the lounge watching his favourite television programme. 'I don't want to carry everything upstairs. I know what to do, I'll hide them all in here.'

Steven squashed his teddy behind the cushions, his books under the video recorder and just managed to squeeze his ball inside mum's best vase. He heard the kitchen door opening and his animals were still all over the floor. Just in time, he posted them one-by-one into mum's sewing box.

'Good boy,' said mum as she walked in. 'What a lovely tidy room!'

---

1 What was Steven doing when mum told him to tidy up his toys? (✔ a box.)

☐ playing with his toys   ☐ reading a book

☐ squashing up his teddy   ☐ watching television

2 Where did Steven hide the following toys? (Join the boxes.)

teddy	in mum's vase
ball	in mum's sewing box
animals	behind the cushion

3 Why did mum say 'Good boy!' to Steven? (Write your answer on the line.)

_____

Honey

Honey is made by bees. Some bees live in beehives but wild bees make their nests in places like trees. This is where bears find honey.

All bees make honeycombs using wax from their bodies. The honeycomb is full of gaps and this is where bees store the honey.

Bee sucking nectar from a flower

Bees make honey from nectar which is a sweet sugary liquid made by flowers. Bees use their mouths to suck up the nectar. They have special mouths that look like tubes so they can reach deep inside the flowers. When bees return to their nests they mix the nectar with a special juice from their mouths. This turns the nectar into honey.

1 Where do bees live? Put a ✔ or ✗ in each box.

in flowers	
in honeycombs	
in trees	
in beehives	

2   What is nectar? (✔ a box.)

☐ special juice   ☐ wax from a bee's body

☐ a sweet liquid   ☐ sugar

3 Where do bees store the honey? (Write your answer on the line.)

_____

Beyond the book

Further activities to support the development of reading and writing
(notes for parents)

- **Act as a good role model** – make sure your child sees you reading and writing regularly at home.

- **Read books together** – taking it in turns to read to each other. Talk about what has been read and ask open questions such as: Why do you think the author used that word or phrase, what would you see if you were there, how would you feel if that happened to you?

- **Write together for a real purpose** – write lists, letters, reminders, messages to each other.

- **Work on story structures together by unpicking the elements of the story at the end** – think about the main characters, the setting and the time, and choose favourite phrases, sentences and words. Discuss the story plot and check to see how the end of the story links back to the beginning.

- **Gain familiarity with instructional texts** – by reading recipes together and making them, reading instructions for 'how to use the video', make-it–yourself furniture etc. Encourage your child to explain orally how something has been done then ask questions – Are you sure that was first? What came next?

- **Listen to radio or television programmes** – that give information then try to match the style, particularly focusing on technical vocabulary.

- **Watch short cartoons or news clips together** – with the sound off and retell the story or event.

- **Play 'Take it in turns'** – tell a story either by saying one word or one sentence each then swapping over.

- **Play 'Join it together'** – player 1 says a phrase or sentence and the other person says a conjunction, e.g. and, because, next, and carries on. You could have some conjunction cards handy as a prop.

- **Retell a story** – changing the character, setting or plot and see what happens.

- **Make a special book** – where quality sentences, phrases and words discovered in written texts are collected. Divide into sections, e.g. found at the beginning, the middle or the end.

- **Play rainbow sentences** – write one in one colour and the next in another – really good for sentence punctuation.

Answers

Capital letters and full stops page 2

1   Goldilocks saw three bowls of porridge. She felt very hungry.

2   One star was extra bright. It had golden rings round it.

Question marks page 3

1   Why did Goldilocks go to the cottage? She sat on the biggest chair but it was too hard. Who likes porridge with salt?

2   How many planets travel round the Sun?
     How long does the Earth take to travel round the Sun?

Exclamation marks page 4

1   Oh dear! That's awful! Look out! What a lovely day!

2   Who ate the porridge? Goodness me! My name is Baby Bear.
     How many stars are in the sky?

Commas in a list page 5

1   … peas, beans, potatoes and carrots; … one, two, three bowls

2   socks, shirts, vests … toothbrush, flannel, hairbrush … coat, scarf, hat …

Speech marks page 6

1   'There she is!' squeaked Baby Bear. 'Starship to mission control,' said Hutch.

2   'Don't press that button!' shouted Star. 'It's all broken!' cried Baby Bear.

Punctuation practice page page 7

Baby Bear's Birthday
It was Baby Bear's birthday. He was excited because Goldilocks was coming to tea. Mother Bear made sandwiches, jelly, biscuits and a cake with five blue candles on the top. Father Bear hung up red, white, green and yellow balloons.
'When will Goldilocks get here?' asked Baby Bear. 'I want my tea!'
'She won't be long now,' replied Mother Bear.
'Here she comes!' shouted Baby Bear and he rushed out to meet her. Splat! He was in such a hurry that he fell over.
'Don't cry,' said Goldilocks, 'Look, I've got you a present.'

Vowels page 8

1   Short vowels = cat, shop, brick, hen, brush;

2   cry, fly, try, sky;   kite, quite;   high, night, light

Blends page 9

1   frog   mask   spring   nest

2   chop = 3; fish = 3; milk = 4; skip = 4; blue = 3; step = 4;
     blend = 5; green = 4; string = 5; stamp = 5

Tricky words   page 10

1   know = no, now; four = our; about = out, bout; one = on; what = hat, at

2   ough

Plurals   page 11

1   flowers, trees, animals; sandwiches, glasses, dishes, boxes

2   tables, books, brushes, shoes

'ed' endings   page 12

1   Just add 'ed' – jump, bump, melt, watch, brush, wish, wait – others double letter

2   The children waited for the spaceship.

'ing' endings   page 13

1   hopping   skipping   riding   taking

2   trying   sleeping   hitting   baking

Spelling practice page   page 14

1   eight, computer, chair, brushes, people, knight, clocks, stairs, crutches;

2   looking, looked; stopping, stopped; taping, taped; crushing, crushed; skipping, skipped; whining, whined; rubbing, rubbed

Playing with words   page 15

1   dark and damp   soft and silky red rocket

2   fire crackled   woofed the dog   waves crashed

Words instead of 'said'   page 16

1   Read the sentences through to decide if the chosen words sounds effective

2   Own collection – keep going with it. Store on disk if a computer available

Pronouns   page 17

1   'They' instead of the second 'the three bears'

2   'It' instead of the second 'the rocket'

3   'He' instead of the second 'Star'

Connectives   page 18

1   but   because

2   Read through for sense.

Time connectives   page 19

1   first, next, finally

2   First of all … After that … Then … Last of all

Sentences   page 20

1   Read through for effect

2   Read through for effect

Checking for sense   page 21

1   but it was   tried the third

2   'are' becomes 'am'   'is' becomes 'am'

How to begin a story   page 22

1   'Why did you do that?' yelled Kim. (q) On the first day of term Jack woke up early. (t)
           Danny didn't want to play football. (n)

2   Read through for sense

Story settings   page 23

1   Safe words – happy, beautiful, white, sparkling, light, warm, soft, peaceful

2   Words from the scary list

Characters   page 24

1, 2, 3   Read through for effectiveness, making sure 'looks like', 'doing' and 'feeling' come
           through clearly

4   Read through

Story endings   page 25

1   Mary wanted a puppy – That's the best present, The clock – So the monster

2   Look for use of words from opening and title

Planning a story   page 26

1   Read through carefully, checking for interest, structure and accuracy

Laying out a letter 2   page 28

1   Check accuracy of address and date

2   Check for consistency of voice – does it remain as I?

Planning a letter   page 29

1   Check for address, date, greeting and signing off

Writing instructions 2   page 31

1   How to look after your pet hamster How to clean your teeth

2   materials

3   Put on your night clothes. Get into bed. Read a story. Turn off the light. Go to sleep.

Planning your instructions   page 32

           Check for heading, materials, logical order of things to be done

Indexes and glossaries   page 33

1   Earth   Moon   Pluto Rocket Sun

2   Earth – planet where we live, Pluto smallest planet, Saturn – planet with rings

Writing an information booklet   page 35

1   Hamster – Go to a well-known pet shop; Stars – Stars are made ;
         Teeth – A lot of the food

2   Keep building and talking about the collection

Planning your information booklet   page 36

1   Check for appropriate title headings on pages with matched text, index, glossary,
         contents, appropriate labelled diagrams

Comprehension – tick the box   page 37

1   Porridge – made from oats

Comprehension – match the boxes   page 38

1   Wild bears – in caves; Rabbits – under the ground; Birds – in trees and bushes

Comprehension – tick and cross   page 39

1   Sweets ✕; milk ✓; fruit ✓; fizzy drink ✕

Comprehension – writing an answer   page 40

1   a pint of boiling water (the answer does not need to be in a sentence)

Comprehension practice – fiction   page 41

1   Watching television

2   Teddy – behind the cushion; Ball – in mum's vase; Animals – in mum's sewing box

3   Because she thought Steven had tidied up his toys properly

Comprehension practice – non-fiction   page 42

1   In trees, In beehives

2   A sweet liquid

3   In gaps in the honeycomb

Glossary of technical terms

Alliteration	the use of the same sound at the start of words occurring near each other - careful Katy cut some cabbage
Blends	the combining of two or more sounds especially at the beginning and end of words – st, str, nt, pr, nd
Comprehension	Understanding the meaning in a text including meaning that is below the surface
Connectives	Words and phrases that link ideas inside sentences and between sentences – at last, although, because, suddenly
Consonants	All the letters of the alphabet except the vowels a, e, i, o, u.
Descriptive words	Adjectives describe things e.g. blue, small, but verbs e.g. slithered and adverbs e.g. hurriedly also add description
Digraph	Two letters representing just one sound – sh, ch, ng, th. Digraphs must not be confused with blends
Fiction	Text that has been invented by the writer. Characters, settings and events are made up but can be based on fact
Non-fiction	Not made up, true/factual. Covers a wide range of texts including recipes, autobiographies, reports, explanations
Nouns	Denotes someone or something. Names of people, places & animals are all nouns, so are words such as kindness, beauty
Pronouns	Words used in place of a noun. They are extremely important in writing to avoid overuse of a particular name
Punctuation	Marks used in writing to help reader's understanding by separating units of meaning e.g. full stops, commas
Speech verbs	The verbs used near dialogue, the most common being said. Alternatives can give more information – spluttered, cried
Tense	Past, present and future tense is indicated by verbs, e.g. ed at the end of a verb indicates past tense. e.g. He played ball.
Vowels	a, e, i, o, u and sometimes y. The spelling of vowel sounds causes many difficulties